Meditation: A Beginner's Guide

MARK CHATTERTON

MEDITATION: A BEGINNER'S GUIDE

BY MARK CHATTERTON

PRINTED BOOK VERSION
ISBN: 978-1-910811-89-4

First published in 2021 by Hadleigh Books, Hadleigh, Essex, SS7 2HA, UK

This book is also available in the following formats: -

Amazon Kindle version – ISBN 978-1-910811-86-3

E-Pub version for Tablet, Smart phone or Kobi - ISBN 978-1-910811-87-0

PDF file for Personal Computer - ISBN 978-1-910811-88-7

www.hadleighbooks.co.uk

Disclaimer: The information presented in this book should not be treated as a substitute for professional medical advice. Always consult a medical practitioner for conditions requiring medical attention. Neither the publisher nor the author can be held responsible for any loss, claim or damage arising out of the use, or misuse, of the suggestions made; the failure to take medical advice; or for any inaccuracies or errors within the text, or for material on third party websites.

CONTENTS

INTRODUCTION

Most people have heard of meditation, but if you asked them, "What do you mean by meditation?" you would get hundreds of different answers. To some it might be sitting quietly and contemplating the world or trying to achieve Enlightenment. To others it might be repeating a special type of mantra or note; whilst to others it could be walking in a forest and breathing in all the sights and sounds of your walk. So, the problem with meditation is that there are so many different types!

Then there is the question of what meditation means for each person. If you add to this mix the various religions, which all practise meditation in some form or other, you will again get a wide spectrum of meditative practises according to which religious tradition you look at. To compound the problem, there are also plenty of people with no religious background at all, both agnostics and atheists who also practise meditation as a health activity. So, it is easy to see that meditation can mean many different things, depending on how you look at it. The main purpose of this book then is to make the practice of meditation much simpler and easier to understand, especially if all this is new to you, so that you too can learn to meditate with ease in a comfortable and non-pressurised way.

The practice of meditation is thousands of years old and has been practised by millions, if not billions of humans over the years. It is practised by adherents of all the main religions as well as those with no religious or spiritual belief. Certain religious and cultural influences have helped to create the main types of meditation that we have today. These all have their place, though not all of them are suitable for a beginner. Some of them are practised by a certain type of person who has been trained by an expert on how best to practise a particular type of meditation. Meditation is a little like the spread Marmite. Some people take to one type of meditation like a duck to water, whilst others may decide that this is not for them.

This book then is designed to help you through this meditation minefield to find the type of meditation that best suits you. Plus, after time you may well find yourself fine tuning your particular type of meditation to "tune in" to your own vibration if you like. What is important though is to be able to understand what meditation actually is; how you can learn to practise it and how it can be of benefit to you. This book will help you to do all these and more.

Perhaps the biggest boost for meditation in modern times was in the 1960's when the Beatles became adherents of the Maharishi Mahesh Yogi, who promoted his particular version of transcendental meditation to the Western world. It was in 1967 during the so-called "Summer of Love" that this happened, and the world immediately heard about meditation; albeit one particular strand of meditation. The following year all four of the Beatles travelled to India to learn more about meditation in the Maharishi's ashram. They were joined by other celebrities of their day including the singer Donovan, Mike Love of the Beach Boys and actress Mia Farrow. This group was accompanied by scores of reporters and photographers who helped to publicise meditation to their readers. From then on meditation became a commonly used word and it began to grow rapidly in the Western world. However, meditation was already practised by many people in the West, both through various religions and because of the lectures of various eastern gurus which helped to wake up the Western world to it.

Traditionally meditation has been seen as being a practice associated with eastern religions like Hinduism, Buddhism and its offshoot Zen Buddhism. Though other eastern based religions like Sikhism, Taoism and Shinto have also included meditation in their religious practice. It is also a practice within both the Jewish, Muslim and Christian religions. With the spread of Christianity throughout Europe and eventually to the New World, meditation as practised by the thousands of monks in their monasteries as part of their contemplation activities also helped to spread meditation throughout the world. Then as people moved around the world more, both through trade and as refugees in some cases, meditation and yoga as used in other religions like Hinduism and Buddhism helped it to spread from the East to the West.

In fact, in our modern and busy world, meditation has now become mainstream in many areas that you wouldn't expect. For example, in some parts of the world in offices and factories there are meditation sessions at the start of the day. Plus, some workers are taught the basics of mindfulness meditation to help them to lower their stress levels. Then in the medical world it has gained a reputation as a way of managing stress and other diseases of the mind like depression, anger and insomnia. If you add to this the evidence from Science, which has shown that meditation can be a useful tool in dealing with depression, chronic pain and heart disease, then it becomes an even more attractive therapy to help us lead healthier and calmer lives

Meditation has also been used in many parts of the world as a means of bringing about change in some way or other. For instance, in Thailand in 2016 there was a mass meditation for peace which involved approximately one million children all meditating for peace together in the Phra Shammakaya Temple. If you find this hard to believe, look it up on the internet and see the amazing pictures of this event. Meditation has also been used in helping people find healing both in themselves and in others. So 'meditation for healing' groups have now become commonplace in many parts of the West.

There are also plenty of celebrities who proudly tell the world that they practise meditation in various ways. These include the musicians Paul McCartney, Madonna and Katy Perry; sports stars like Formula 1 racing driver, Lewis Hamilton and tennis player Novak Djokovic; the broadcaster Oprah Winfrey; and the actors Clint Eastwood and Tom Hanks. But it's not just the celebrities who meditate, there are also many successful businessmen and women who do it. They even practise meditation in the US marines so I'm told, to help them to focus better when they are on the front line! In the recent Coronavirus pandemic, many people started to try meditation as a way of finding peace and calmness with all the uncertainty going on in their lives, especially when they found they had more time on their hands during lockdowns.

Meditation is now well and truly established as an activity practised by millions of people worldwide. I myself can vouch for the way it has helped me over the years. For example, in my driving I am now much calmer when I drive and don't get upset when other drivers drive badly in front of me! I am also much calmer when there is a crisis and react to it in a much more rational way, knowing that in the words of John Lennon, "There's no problems; only solutions!" In reading this book I hope that you will discover that meditation is not a weird or way out thing practised by other weird and way out people, but rather an activity that can be part of your daily routine. As such it will help you to lead a happier, calmer and healthier lifestyle.

Mark Chatterton

November 2020

1 WHAT IS MEDITATION?

The most obvious question to ask at the start of this book is, "Just what do you mean by meditation?" Giving a precise definition of what constitutes meditation is quite a hard thing to do. Most traditions of meditation have their own definition which can vary quite considerably from one to another. There are many definitions to be found on the Internet. For example, the Cambridge Dictionary states that meditation is "the act of giving your attention to only one thing, either as a religious activity or as a way of becoming calm and relaxed". The Oxford Reference website sees meditation as being "techniques and practices designed to concentrate and focus the mind". However, the best definitions of meditation that I have found is this one from the Everyday Health website which seems to sum up in a few sentences what meditation is all about. Here it is....

"Meditation is the practice of thinking deeply or focusing one's mind for a period of time. This can be done in silence or with the help of chanting, and is done for a number of reasons, ranging from religious or spiritual purposes to a method for evoking relaxation".

So, the main facets of meditation are using your mind to focus on something specific, which could be for relaxation or spiritual purposes. Of course, not everyone will be happy with this definition, but I believe for the purposes of this book this definition fits in with what I am about to teach you about meditation.

Another shorter definition that I use is from a phrase that we use in everyday speech, which when you think of it also sums up what meditation is all about, but in a more concise way. We often hear this phrase, perhaps from a teacher, or your boss, or your parents and that is, "Will you put your mind to it!" By that they mean "Get on with the task in hand....concentrate....stop what you're thinking/doing and concentrate on what you should be doing!" So, in a way this short phrase, "Put your mind to it", best sums up meditation in four words! It means that you are focussing on something intently with your mind and that is what meditation is basically about.

Many people think of meditation as being a religious act or a religious practice. Certainly, meditation is practised by adherents of every religion that there are, yet it is also practised by millions of people the world over who would say that they are not in the slightest bit religious. This latter group includes the author of this book!

This book is written primarily for those of you who are not religious and who want to find out about meditation free of religious dogma and rules. It is basically about meditation that is straightforward and easy to understand. It does involve some sort of commitment from you the reader if you want to practise meditation to a basic standard. Once you have learnt the basics, you will be able to progress to a higher and more proficient level.

Perhaps the best analogy of learning to practise meditation is that of learning to swim. In order to learn to swim you have to get into the water first of all. Sure, you can learn some of the basic strokes and how you should swim on land, but it is only when you get into the water that you can really start to learn to swim. The same goes for meditation. You can read all about it and what it involves, but until you start to actually do it, you can't really learn to meditate.

Learning to meditate will involve a commitment from you to want to succeed at it, despite what practising meditation involves. Yet when you push yourself out into the swimming pool or lake and start to swim, you realise that it is possible to swim. The same goes for meditation. Once you start to practise meditation, it gradually becomes easier to do and with practice will become second nature.

Without a doubt the benefits are worth it, such as peace of mind, calmness, a greater ability to cope with all that life throws at you and so on. I will go into more detail about these benefits in the next chapter. I actually find that if I miss doing my meditation for whatever reason, I find that something is missing in my life. It's not guilt, but an emptiness that I feel. It's now an everyday part of me, which I like to do, need to do even, so that I am able to function as a human being in the best possible way.

The different types of meditation

Before I go onto discuss what different types of meditation there are, I must mention the fact that some religious traditions divide meditation up into two basic groups. These two groups of meditation are known as "Stabilizing Meditation" and "Analytical Meditation".
With Stabilizing Meditation, the idea is to stabilize or still your mind so that it goes deeper into the meditation and you eventually come into a state of bliss or perfect peace. This might be achieved by repeating a word or mantra over and over again, or constantly looking at an object or picture.
With Analytical Meditation you would be looking at the picture or thinking about the word, so that you analyse it such a way that you begin to understand everything about it. This might involve thinking about how this picture or object came into being, what uses it has or how it is beneficial to you. As a result, you will come to have a greater understanding of how this picture or object fits into the world or the scheme of things.
To sum up, stabilizing meditation calms the mind, whilst analytical meditation changes the mind. It might be prudent to bear

in mind these two versions of meditation as we discuss some of the various types of meditation that there are.

Having explained about the two groups of meditation, I will now go through the main types of meditation. Again, this number varies according to which tradition you are using. Some teach that there are just two types of meditation, whilst others say there are four and others say six or seven. Obviously, this number can vary according to who says it, so I have provided details of eight main types of meditation, which I think sum up the main types. Bear in mind that one type of meditation may include some of the others, or some may actually be the same type of meditation by a different name. So here are the main types according to me!

1) Mindfulness Meditation

Mindfulness meditation or just plain "Mindfulness" is perhaps the most common and well-known version of meditation. It is also the one with the most different definitions! At its most basic it is the state of being mindful or aware of something. In more detail it is about being in the present moment observing what is going on all around you, but not reacting to it or judging it. This is like watching your thoughts go past you on a conveyor belt if you like. You observe them, but don't actually react to them, such as thinking, "I must do this as a result of this happening"; or "I will never achieve this as I'm just not cut out for it". Instead with mindfulness meditation (or "insight meditation" as some call it) you may well see all these different thoughts in your mind. But you learn to rise above them and not react to them in your normal way with worry, stress, or fear. Instead, you will learn to "go with the flow" and let them pass through you in a way where you don't react, but instead accept them and then move on. It's a type of processing factory for your brain if you like. You sort out your thoughts and deal with them in such a way that you are able to overcome the fear, worry or stress that they might bring you.

2) Guided Meditation

With guided meditation you go into a state of meditation with someone leading you through this process. This may be in a one to one situation or in a group situation with someone leading or "guiding" you through the meditation. The guide could also be guiding you remotely through a tape or a CD; an app from the internet, or through a social media platform like Zoom or Skype.

The leader will start by getting you to relax and get your mind focussed on your breathing. He or she will then lead or "guide" you into a meditative state, perhaps by taking you on a journey to a safe place in your mind where you can deal with a problem that is bugging you, or alternatively guide you to focus on a certain concept, such as Love or Peace and then help you to experience this at a very deep level.

If you are a beginner with meditation, or if you prefer to be guided in this way then this type of meditation will suit you. If on the other hand you prefer not to be told what to do or are an independent type of person you will probably give this type of meditation a miss.

3) Transcendental Meditation

As mentioned in the Introduction this type of meditation was popularised in the West in the 1960's, partly through the influence of the Beatles. It comes from India and is based on Hindu philosophy. "TM" as it is commonly known, involves the participant repeating a unique mantra given to him/her, which they repeat in their mind until they begin to feel their mind moving away from the present world and into a higher state of consciousness. Participants are encouraged to do this twice a day for about twenty minutes and gradually they will feel a change in their minds where they achieve a blissful state. This in turn helps them cope better with everyday life and how they react to it.

4) Chakra meditation

This is a type of meditation that involves using the chakras, a set of invisible energy fields scattered throughout the body. Most teachers of this form of meditation say that there are seven main chakras in the body and when you have an illness in your body this is due to one or more of your chakras being out of balance or sync. The chakra meditation is involved with re-balancing your chakras one by one so that your body is well and healthy again. Some people choose to use the colours associated with each chakra to complete this meditation. A whole chapter is devoted to the chakras and this type of meditation later on in the book.

5) Yoga Meditation

Basically, this is a type of meditation you do whilst practising yoga. By yoga I mean the practice of exercising both the body and mind through a set of specific exercises known as "poses" which are combined with various breathing techniques. Meditation is added to the mix to help with the overall experience, which can help lead to better balance, reduced stress, stronger bones and a calmer you.

6) Loving Kindness Meditation or Metta Meditation

This is concerned with sending out loving kindness to other people or things, and receiving loving kindness back from loved ones, for example. To do this you must first get your body and mind into a meditative state. Then through a series of visualisations and mantras you both give out and receive loving kindness. It can be extended to other people, be they acquaintances, enemies, politicians, or all people in the world. The aim is to make you feel calmer, happier, and kinder, as what you give out, so you will receive.

7) Vipassana Meditation

This is a form of meditation which comes from Buddhism and means "without seeing" or having "insight". It concentrates on the interconnection between the mind and the body and how the mind can be trained and purified. It tends to concentrate on how you can overcome your physical desires through this type of meditation, which is done in silence for long periods of time. It is believed to be the oldest form of Buddhist meditation practice and is very popular in India, though it is also growing as a meditative practice in the West.

8) Walking Meditation

As the name suggests this is a type of meditation you can do whilst walking at the same time as meditating. Obviously, this is something that you do with your eyes open for obvious reasons! The walking meditation can be done in an urban environment such as in a town centre, or out in the countryside, such as walking in a wood or by a river. Or you could do it whilst walking around your house if have difficulty in going out. The important thing is to focus on both your breathing and the way you walk, getting into a natural rhythm. Then once you are comfortable with these you can start to focus on both the sights, sounds and smells around you. The idea is that you don't just have to be sitting still to meditate, but rather you can meditate just as well outside as you move about. This type of meditation can be suitable for those people who lead busy lives and perhaps only have the time to meditate in their lunch hours. This won't work if you are rushing to catch a train or are on your way to an important appointment. But if you are in a situation where you have some spare time, this could work for some people.

These then are some of the most popular and important types of meditation groups. Of course, there may be others which you can think of or even practise, but for the purposes of this book these are the ones which I think are most relevant. I shall now look at the various benefits of meditation in the next chapter, along with the various scientific studies on them.

2 THE BENEFITS OF MEDITATION

Why do you need to practise meditation? What's in it for me? Is it really that good? Will it help me to be calmer? Can it help with my feelings of depression? Surely, I don't need to do it as my life is busy enough? These are all questions that you may well be asking about meditation. There's probably more that you can think of, but in order to calm your fears let's look at some of the benefits of meditation and how it can help you. Many of these claims have been backed up by scientific studies, which I will include in the text. So hopefully this chapter will help allay your fears, banish your doubts and help you to understand why practising meditation is good for you.

The Benefits of Meditation

The benefits of meditation are many and worth the effort of practising it. Here is a list of some of the main benefits of meditation and in most cases the results of science-based research behind these benefits.

It helps you to become calmer and less stressed

The most obvious benefit of meditation is that it helps you to be calmer. It gives you an inner peace which you can take with you wherever you go and whatever situation you are in. It can help you to become calmer and more peaceful. Maybe you are one of these people who are forever rushing around. You never seem to have time to relax, or when you do relax it is of the variety where you are still moving about, such as playing a sport or travelling to somewhere else. Practising meditation will first of all teach you to sit still for a change and stop rushing here there and everywhere! The discipline of meditation will teach you to slow down and that there is more to life than your particular hectic lifestyle.

The stress hormone cortisol is stimulated by a wide variety of triggers in our daily lives. This in turn releases inflammatory chemicals called cytokines which can cause depression and anxiety, sleep loss and high blood pressure. In 2012 an eight-week study into the effects of mindfulness meditation by various scientists as the University of Wisconsin-Madison and Ohio State University was shown to reduce this inflammation response.

It helps you to become more content and less anxious

Apart from the fact that meditation can help you to reduce the stress within you, it can also help you to become a much happier person. Once you start practising meditation on a regular basis you will find that you become not just a calmer person, but also a happier one, more content with life. Why? It is because meditation helps you to not only slow down but also to take stock of your life and your lifestyle. In doing so, you become less anxious about life and start to enjoy it more. Several studies have shown this too. One in 2018 at Michigan Technological University in the USA found a clear reduction in anxiety after an hour-long meditation session involving fourteen participants. Their anxiety scores were reduced even more after a week of such sessions.

It helps you to become a more confident and positive person

Many people believe, (myself included), that regular practise of meditation will help you to have a more positive outlook on life, giving you better emotional health. I would say that since I started practising meditation I have stopped worrying considerably.

Continued meditation practice has been shown to help people with social anxiety. A 2009 study at Stanford University in California found that fourteen people with social anxiety disorder who did two months of meditation training reported both decreased anxiety and increased self-esteem after completing the programme.

It helps to cut down on pain levels in the body

Many people who regularly practise meditation say that existing pain seems to lessen either during or after the meditation session. Obviously, the level of pain that you feel is connected with your state of mind. This can get worse when you worry or get stressed, so if you meditate the calmer you become, which can help reduce the level of pain that you are feeling. This has been borne out by several scientific studies. For example, a June 2017 study by scientists at Georgia Southern University and Northwestern University found that meditation was a useful inhibitor of transient receptor potential channels in patients suffering from Irritable Bowel Syndrome. In other words, it helped to reduce the level of pain in patients.

It helps you to sleep better

Some studies have shown that regular meditation can help to improve your sleep as many of us have problems sleeping properly at some point in our lives. When you meditate you learn to overcome the thought patterns that can take over your mind when you are trying to tune into your meditative state. This skill can in turn be used to calm your mind down and relax your body as you drop off to sleep. A 2014 by several universities in the USA and Canada involving fifty-four adults with chronic insomnia found that those who regularly used mindfulness meditation stayed asleep for longer periods than those who did not.

It helps you to appreciate those around you more

By regularly practising meditation many people believe that you start to appreciate those around you more. Not just the members of your immediate family, but also those people who maybe helping you in some way or other, such as doctors and nurses, delivery drivers, council workers, teachers, and so one. You begin to realise that everyone is connected to you in some way and you see more clearly how you fit into the world around you. You see that you are not just a number, or a cog in a larger wheel, but a human being with his or her own mind who can think for themselves.

As a result of this you start to feel more positive about the world you live in and appreciative of other people. You also start to generate kind thoughts to others. This is borne out by studies into the effects of loving-kindness or metta meditation. One 2011 study at Boston University found that the regular practice of loving-kindness meditation and compassion meditation led to positive emotional states of kindness and compassion.

It can help you to have better focus and concentration levels

It goes without saying that regular meditation teaches you to still your mind and focus on the meditation experience. So, it is not surprising that scientific studies have shown this to be the case in everyday life. A 2016 study by researchers at Carnegie Mellon University in Pittsburgh in the USA found that meditation can help improve people's levels of concentration and decision making. They studied 35 unemployed adults who were looking for work, split into two groups. One group did mindfulness meditation each day during a three-day period, whilst the other group didn't. Both groups had their brains scanned before and after the study. There was an increase in brain connectivity in the parts of the brain that control attention in the group that did the meditation, whilst this did not occur in the other group.

It helps you to understand more about yourself

Those who practise the form of meditation known as "self-inquiry meditation" where you explore your inner self as well as your place in the world, say that it teaches them to be more self-aware. This can be true of other types of meditation where you go "inside" yourself and learn things about you that you didn't know about or that you were keeping hidden, perhaps through shame or embarrassment. Meditation gives you the courage to face up to your inner fears and thus deal with them in a constructive way. You also learn to be more outgoing, as you realise that you are "not an island", but part of a bigger picture of human existence. In a 2019 study organised by the University of Pittsburgh involving 153 people using a mindfulness meditation app for two weeks, it was found that participants started to have increased social contact compared with those in the control group. They also felt less lonely.

It helps you to love yourself more

Connected with the above benefit of regular meditation practice is the notion of "loving oneself". This is where you come to realise that you accept who you are with all your faults, attitudes and fears. You may not like the way you look or the way you behave, yet through regular meditation you learn to overcome these negative attitudes. As a result, you may start to exercise more; perhaps taking up yoga or running. Or you may start to eat more healthy foods and drop those that aren't healthy. There is a guided meditation about this subject later on in the book in the chapter on guided meditations.

It helps you to appreciate Nature

One benefit of doing regular meditation is that I have come to have a better appreciation of the natural world around me. I now enjoy going for walks in the woods near to where I live and observing all the birds flying about or spotting the occasional wild animal. I also enjoy visiting the coast and finding the movement of the waves very relaxing. It could be that you start to walk regularly in the local park if you haven't got a garden, observing the trees, birds and animals there. Or perhaps that you start doing a bit of gardening, growing flowers, or fruit and vegetables, all the while appreciating the way that nature works.

It can help you to overcome addictions

The more you become skilled and adept at meditation, the more you should be able to control and even overcome the triggers that are there in your mind for addictions. These could be all sorts of things such as alcohol dependency, food cravings or drug use. So, by doing meditation you are altering the brain receptors that are associated with these sorts of addictions. You are now able to notice the desire within you to have that drink or take that drug, and instead of giving in to it, you overcome the desire instead. A 2017 study by the Friends Research Institute of Baltimore of 60 people who were receiving treatment for alcohol use disorder, found that by practising transcendental meditation over a period of three months their desire for alcohol and the stress it caused was reduced.

These are just some of the possible benefits from the regular practice of meditation. Others that I have not discussed include the possibility that it can reduce your blood pressure, as well as reduce memory loss in your older years. I am not saying that meditation works in every example for every person who does it, but from the above evidence from scientific studies and my own experience, meditation is worth checking out if you suffer from any of the above conditions. Or if you merely want to slow down and appreciate your life more, then meditation will certainly help you to do so.

3 GETTING READY FOR MEDITATION

The three "S's"

Before I go into detail about how you actually prepare for a meditation, I would like to mention the three "S's". This is the name I have given to a useful key to bear in mind whenever you meditate. The three "S's" stand for Silence, Stillness and Something and are what I say are needed for the best meditation experience. Silence and Stillness are the best ways of conducting your meditation sessions, whilst "Something" is what you would expect to get out of your meditation sessions. It is a good idea to keep these in mind when you start to practise meditation. I will go into them into more detail about them below, but for now it is worth bearing in mind these three "S's".

Having a routine

When you first begin to meditate it can be quite daunting for some people. Not knowing what to expect and what it is going to be like. You might be thinking, "Is this right for me?", or "What am I getting myself into?" I always say to my students it will help you considerably if you can get yourself into some sort of routine to begin with. By this I mean meditating at a set or regular time each day, as well as using the various tools which I set out below. This will not only help you to move over from your everyday life into your meditation life, but also help meditation to become something you do quite naturally, rather than as a "forced" activity.

Getting into a routine will help your meditation practice significantly. If you are practising meditation on a daily basis at roughly the same time of the day you will soon be able to slip easily into it, rather than struggle to settle down and start it. Most people find that they prefer to do their meditation in the morning as opposed to the afternoon or evening. This is mainly because the stresses and strains of the day can soon start to get in the way of doing meditation. Plus, it can set you up for the rest of the day. Once you are at work or busy travelling around, you just don't have the time or inclination to practice meditation. Of course, if the morning is just too busy, then later on in the day may sit you better. I would say don't leave it until just before bedtime though, as more than likely in your relaxed state of meditation you may well fall asleep!

Finding the best place to use for your meditation

The location of the place where you are going to meditate is also important. It should be somewhere where you will feel at ease in yourself and where you will not be disturbed. When you meditate you need to be in a place where you can focus easily on the meditation, so that it becomes second nature to you. If you are in a place where you feel comfortable, both physically and emotionally then the meditation will work much better for you.

The obvious place for most people is usually a room somewhere within your house. This may well be your lounge or living room, where you can perhaps sit on a settee, or a comfy chair? It might be a bedroom, maybe sitting up on your bed itself, or in a chair in the bedroom. Or it might be somewhere outside. If you are lucky enough to have a garden, you might choose to meditate in a summer house, or even a shed that you have prepared.

I myself prefer to meditate in my garage! It's not what you think though. My garage was built in the garden by a previous owner, even though there is no side access to it for a car. I believe he used it as a workshop for his motorbikes. I myself have transformed it into a special room with a carpet, a settee and lots of colourful pictures on the walls so that I have made my own mark on it. With the door open it faces out onto the lawn looking at two large trees, so that when it is warm you could almost think that you are outside in Nature.

In fact, many people who meditate prefer to be outside when they mediate, as they feel they are closer to nature there, or perhaps the inside of their house is just too noisy for them to concentrate on meditating. So, if this is you, you might like to meditate in a public park or out somewhere in the countryside where you are much closer to Nature than inside a house.

It could also be when you are on a journey perhaps? This could be on a train or a coach as you make a journey. I myself have meditated on trains lots of times, sometimes just looking out of the window as the countryside goes past, or sometimes with my eyes closed. If you are able to cut out the people and noises outside you, there is no reason why you can't meditate in a place like this. I know of some people who wear headphones, giving the impression that they are listening to music, when in fact they are meditating! Or maybe they could be listening to a guided meditation via their smart phone.

You can also meditate outside as you go for a walk, perhaps through a wood or along a riverbank. I will go into this type of meditation in more detail in the next chapter.

The important thing is for you to be both happy and comfortable in the place you choose to have your meditation, so that it becomes a regular, effortless, and positive experience for you.

Getting rid of possible distractions

Having found the best place for your meditation, it is also important that you make sure that there are no possible distractions to your meditation. For example, it might be that you are expecting the postman to be coming round with a parcel, so you can't really concentrate. Maybe best wait until he or she has been? Or it could be a pet like a cat or a dog who is vying for your attention. This would be distracting for any person, so you would need to think of something to take their mind off you and onto something else, like having something to eat, or giving them a toy to play with.

If there is background noise like the birds singing, it might be easier to accept that and still get on with your meditation. I find that often happens to me when I am meditating in my garage, yet I have come to accept it as part of my meditation practice. If something like that is going to bother you, then maybe you need to get some ear plugs or something that will shut out the noise. Perhaps some gentle music that could be playing in the background might help. Gradually the more you practise meditation, the easier it becomes to get into the meditative state.

Getting into a comfortable position

One of the most important things when you are meditating is to make sure you are sitting in a comfortable position. There is nothing more off-putting than trying to meditate when you don't feel comfortable, either physically or in your mind. We will deal with the second one later, but for now I will discuss how to make sure that you are comfortable.

The traditional position for meditating that most people tend to have in their mind is that of a person sitting in the "Lotus Position" where their legs are crossed, tucked into each other, their back is straight, and their hands are pressed together as though in prayer. Let me tell you that I have never used this position for meditating and probably never will. For a start there is no way that I could get my feet to tuck in under my knees. I'm sure I would end up in hospital if I tried! Seeing a picture of person sitting in this position with the words "meditation" or "meditating" underneath it tends to give a false impression of meditation to the world at large. This position comes from Yoga and more particularly the Buddhist religion where many people learn to sit in this position from an early age when their bones and muscles are more supple than the majority of us. Sure, there are some people in the Western world who are able to sit in this position, but I would say it is not necessary to be in this position to practise meditation.

I would say that the first thing you need to be in a comfortable position is a nice comfy chair, preferably with a high back. I realise that not everyone will have a chair like this in their house. Perhaps they associate a chair like this with an old person sitting in one in a care home and this puts them off. Or they simply cannot afford one. If this is the case, then either an ordinary chair that you use to sit at a table with or even a well packed cushion will do. The important thing here is to support your back and your head, so if you choose the latter types it might be worth leaning up against a wall when you meditate. You could also put a cushion behind your head if you like to give you something soft between your head and a hard wall. You don't have to do this of course, especially if you have a strong back and don't mind sitting upright for a certain length of time.

If you are practising meditation outside, many people like to sit under a tree with their back leaning against the trunk. Again, one or two cushions here might be helpful, but it is up to you whether to have cushions or not. If you have a tree or two in your garden this can be a great place to do your meditation, especially in the spring or summer, but if you are doing this in a public place such as a park or in some woods please consider your safety here, especially if you have your eyes closed. If there are two or more of you then that might be more suitable, but if you are by yourself then remember that you might be putting yourself in a vulnerable position here.

Getting into the right mood

Now having sorted out where you will meditate and where you will be sitting, it is time for you to get into the right mood for meditation, or as some people say, "get into the zone". Quite often we can easily get disturbed in our minds by an issue or an event that has happened the day before, which can affect our meditation. So, as we get ready to meditate, we can't get that issue out of our minds. It might be an argument that we've had with someone, something on the news or something not turning out as we'd expected. This then plays on our mind and gets in the way of our meditation. Just how do you drag your mind away from these various distractions?

You might like to play some relaxing music either before you start, or even all the way through your meditation if you so wish. (See below) This music should be of the quiet sort obviously, which you associate with calming you down and making you feel good. Or you could read a favourite poem or a few lines from a passage from a book that inspires you. Some people have poems or sayings on their wall in a frame which they can read before they start their meditation. Or you could perhaps have a picture or photograph of some natural scene that you could look at for a minute or so before you start to help you focus better?

Using background music

Maybe you are one of those people who seem to thrive on background noise in their lives and "just get on with it". So, the concept of sitting quietly in silence maybe anathema to you? A lot of people find that having some form of background music playing whilst they are meditating actually enhances their experience. This is usually instrumental in nature, though some people find that listening to a particular song with suitable lyrics at the start of their meditation "gets them in the mood" for their meditation. The choice is yours. Perhaps this is something that you might like to experiment with as you start to get into meditation? There are a whole host of tunes available for you to download or listen to on the internet. Maybe try listening to some of these at first to see if any of them rock your boat? Don't forget that as they are written with meditation and contemplation in mind they may well be on a loop and repeat the basic tune again and again. This might be irritating or even off putting for some people, so take your time before you decide to buy any music.

The use of silence in meditation

Having just written about having background music to help you with your meditation, I am now going to say the opposite and talk about being silent in your meditations! Whilst some people do like a little background music when they meditate, I would say the vast majority prefer to practise their meditations in complete silence. Why? Because silence is the best way to go into yourself when you meditate. Silence is the first of the three "S's" as I call them, which are needed to have the best meditation experience I reckon. If you meditate without any distractions to put you off what you are doing, you can move into the zone that you need to be in to meditate quite quickly.

Meditating as you walk

Some people believe that it is possible to meditate as you walk. This obviously involves having your eyes open, so it is a different sort of meditation than the traditional types. This is something that I do on the odd occasion, which makes a nice change and is something that you can do at any time of the year, though summer is best for obvious reasons. I have gone into more detail about this in the chapter on Guided Meditation.

What if you can't get it together?

What if your mind is all at sixes and sevens, and you just can't get into the right frame of mind to do your meditation? Well, if you have honestly tried to get on with your meditation and you just can't get going, maybe it is best to leave it for the time being. Maybe you could leave it for half an hour if you like and then come back and see how you feel then? Perhaps the break might help you to get your mindset in the right frame? Or you might want to leave it altogether and come back to your meditation the next day? It could be that something is on your mind so much that it just won't go away. Somehow this needs to be sorted or you will continue in this frame of mind all day long. Maybe have a chat with someone? Or think things through in a conscious, thorough way until you find peace in your mind. I would say there is no point in trying to do a meditation when your brain and mind are just not where they should be.

The other thing that can stop you meditating is that you become so relaxed in your meditation that you actually fall asleep! This has happened to me on a number of occasions and it has been a battle to stay awake. In a situation like this you are obviously very tired and in need of a sleep. Maybe it would be best to go and lie down on your bed and have a quick nap until you feel refreshed enough to continue with your meditation. There is no point in meditating if you are just going to go to sleep.

There is also a "trick" that I use and that is to focus on a particular colour to get me focussed ad take my mind off my other thoughts. I discuss this in the next chapter and in the chapter on using colours in your meditations.

4 PRACTISING MEDITATION

What are you expecting from your meditation?

Most people when they practise meditation go into it expecting to get something out of it. This is where the third of my three "S's" comes in. What "something" do you think or hope that you will get out of it? It might be an answer to a problem that you are facing, or just getting a little peace or stillness into your life. There is no harm in asking the Universe, your Higher Self, God, or whatever you believe in for something to come out of your meditation practice. These are all things concerning the Present, i.e., what is happening in your life right now. So, your aim in your meditation might be to achieve some sort of state of mind; be it peace, bliss, calmness and so on.

On the other hand, it might be that you are looking to achieve something in the near future to happen in your life, such as a change of job, finding a new partner, or moving to a different place and finding new friends. Again, I would say that focussing on the future is just as valid in your meditation experience. To help you understand this more, I talk about affirmations and visualisations just below.

Before that I will briefly mention another aspect of meditation that some people prefer to do and that is to have a clear mind. This means that in your meditation you empty your mind altogether of all the things that are going on in it. This might be your brain chattering away with a hundred and one different things, all of them concerned with you in the outside world. It could be worrying about your children, or your parents; being concerned with something going on in your workplace; or perhaps being worried about your finances.

Whatever is on your mind as you start your meditation should be cleared away so that you can focus on the emptiness if you like, that is in you. People say that by doing this they can focus much more easily and then both enjoy and benefit from their meditation. I will go into this in more detail below.

Using Affirmations

Affirmations are powerful tools which you can use when you practise meditation as they help you to focus more easily on the subject of your meditation. What exactly is an affirmation? It is saying out loud something with conviction that you believe in or would like to happen in the future. This isn't just something that you can use in your meditations though; it is also a tool that you can use in your everyday life. For example, when you are about to take an important exam and you are quite nervous about it. You might say the affirmation, "I am going to stay calm and do really well in this exam", or "I am going to pass this exam with flying colours!"

When you use an affirmation, you are telling your subconscious self that this is the way that you want to behave, or this is the outcome that you would like to happen.

This can apply in your meditations as well. Here are some examples of affirmations that you could use as you are about to begin your meditation. You could say, "Today I would like to find the answer to the question that I have about......", or "In my meditation today I am going to find inner peace", or "I would like to gain a clearer vision of where I am going in life". There are literally hundreds of different affirmations that you could use at the start of your meditation. Basically, you are helping your subconscious to not only focus your mind on the meditation, but also to help you see the answer to a problem you have or a direction you want to go in.

One question I often get asked is, "Do I have to say my affirmation out loud? Couldn't I just think it in my mind?" Yes, you can just think it in your mind if you like, though I would say it will be a lot more powerful for you if you do speak your affirmation.

Using Visualisations

Visualisations are another important tool that you can use in your meditations if you so wish. Just as an affirmation is something that you say – either out loud or in thought, so a visualisation is a picture that you create in your mind of something that you would like to happen in your life. It might be a new house that you hope to move to in the future, or it might be the perfect partner that you are looking for. Perhaps it is merely the thought of being content or at peace over something. With this type of visualisation, you need to think of the various things that help to make you content or peaceful. Once you have this picture or vision in your mind, hold it there and see where your mind takes you.

Using Prayer

What about prayer? Can you use this in your meditation practice? Isn't this a type of affirmation? If you have a religious faith, or at least if you are of a spiritual bent, there is no reason why you can't say a short prayer before you begin your meditation. You could ask for calm and peace of mind as you begin your meditation, or you could ask that a specific problem in your life can be sorted out in your mind whilst you are in your meditation. Or at least ask to be shown the way forward and perhaps the way to resolve the issue. Sometimes you might pray for someone else who needs your prayers and so your meditation is your way of sending help or healing to this particular person. So, to sum up, yes, prayer is a type of affirmation, only with a religious or spiritual side to it.

Sitting still

This is the second of the three S's that I mentioned earlier. If you are sitting still, then this is half the battle as you can concentrate more on your breathing and your thoughts. As long as you are feeling comfortable wherever you are sitting, be it in a chair, on a cushion, or on the floor, then you can ease into your meditation much more easily.

You can then gather your thoughts before you start your meditation. This might be something that is on your mind and as you become more experienced with meditation, you will be able to dismiss these thoughts which can be distractions at first. So, the trick is to be able to stop the endless flow of thoughts that are filling your head. That is why getting your breathing into a steady rhythm can help you get through this stage. If you are focussing on the various events happening later that day, or something someone may have said to you, either positive or negative, these can easily form a barrier to your meditative practice.

The idea of "gathering your thoughts" could be seen as picking up each thought and putting it into a large bag from which it can't escape! I know it may sound a bit silly, but this use of visualisation can help you to become more focussed as you prepare to start your meditation.

Using colours or objects to help you focus

As a way of moving away from the busy world that you live in through to the calm state of meditation you may find this transition phase quite difficult to achieve. To help with this transition some people, including myself use a tool to help them move from the one mindset to the other. For me this is using colour to help me focus on the meditative state. I have gone into great detail about this in the next chapter about how colours can be used in this way, so I won't discuss it here.

However, it is not just colours that you can use to achieve this. Some people like to look at or concentrate on a particular object to help them to get into the meditative state. One of the most common objects that people use is a statute of the Buddha sitting cross-legged in the lotus position meditating. I would guess that this vision spurs people on to do the same, or at least try to emulate him!

This is only one of endless objects that you can use. People of a particular religion may use images or icons of that religion's founders or gods perhaps. Or some sacred or holy words might be used. If you are not in any way religious, you could look at a nice picture or photograph of something calming like a sunset or scene from Nature. Or again look at the words of an inspiring poem to get you in the mood. Or what about something from nature like a tree, flower, animal, or bird?

Remember these are not part of your meditation (unless you want them to be), but more of a means to an end to guide you through the door and into the meditation place.

Breathing

As you get into your meditative state it is both important and helpful for you to concentrate on your breathing. Breathing in a certain way helps to relax you. Think of a doctor or some other medical person saying "Take a couple of deep breaths" to someone when they have had a shock or an accident. This is because breathing slowly and deeply can help slow the heart rate down and so calm your whole body. This concept is also useful to you as you start your meditation. So, breathing in a conscious way helps you to relax and thus ease you gently into your meditative state.

The best way of breathing as you start your meditation is to breathe quite deeply in through your nose and then slowly exhale through your nose. If you do this slowly and regularly for a minute or two you will find that your body and your mind start to relax. If your eyes are closed as well, this will help you even more. The more your practise this as you begin your meditation you will soon start to do this without conscious thought, and it will become a natural thing that you do when you meditate.

As an alternative to this some people prefer to exhale through their open mouths. They do this as they see positive energy going into their bodies and negative energy coming out. If you want to try this that's fine, though I would suggest not to do it for too long – a minute or two at the most - as I find you tend to breathe more deeply than you need to do. The key to success here is slow, deep breaths which move you into a relaxed state.

Focusing your mind

If you are new to meditation this part can be quite difficult to achieve at first. Perhaps you are one of those people who are constantly on the go, rushing from place to place, meeting to meeting, and you find it incredibly hard to slow down? How on earth do you get yourself into a frame of mind to start your meditation, let alone get into it properly? The answer lies perhaps in doing your meditation at the start of the day before all the madness starts. Or maybe at the end of the day when things have quietened down, though your mind might not be in the best state to do a meditation.

Also, if you can start by getting your breathing sorted, that is half the battle. The other half is to get your mind focussed away from all your cares and the stresses of the day. This is where you could focus on one thing to calm your brain. Focusing on a particular colour at this stage can be helpful. (See next chapter on how to this). Or you could try this visualisation exercise. Imagine that you are floating down a river, either in a boat, or just lying on your back in the river. Don't have a fast-flowing river as that will not calm you down. Instead imagine a very slow flowing river, or if you like imagine that the river has flowed into a lake and it is dead calm. If you can do this in your mind you have managed to start your meditation. Now see if you can imagine your self being still in this flat lake and as you do this, so your mind becomes still, and all your thoughts cease. Now we are getting somewhere.

Starting your meditation

We are now getting to the core of this book and that is actually meditating! At this stage you should be sitting still, comfortable in your seat, with silence all around you. As you start your meditation session some people like to have a marker indicating that the session is starting. For those who are spiritually inclined this might be opening your Third Eye, or Third Eye Chakra to let in the energy. Or it might be saying a short prayer asking for guidance or help that you can sort things out in your meditation. For others it might be a thought that the meditation is just starting, or perhaps it will be just getting on with it!

The meditation itself

Finally, we are now in the meditation itself. The first thing to be aware of is your breathing. It should by now be slow, but steady, calming you with each breath. You should hopefully be feeling calm, with perhaps an air of expectation. Now just sit in silence with no thoughts at all. There are now two ways you can now go. The first is the mindfulness way. The second is the emptiness way.

With the mindfulness option, you might start by thinking about some problem or issue that you have. Rather than get drawn in by it, mentally withdraw from it, move away and imagine that you are now looking down on it. In this position the issue doesn't look as bad as you first thought, and you can see that you are in control of it and not the other way round. In this state decide what you are going to do with it. Is there a solution to it that you haven't thought about yet? You can ask for help now if you wish or say to yourself that you will overcome this particular problem. Now imagine that you are wrapping up the problem and putting it out of the way. As you move it to one side the problem is ceasing to be a problem and it is no longer causing you grief. Now that it has gone you are starting to feel more peaceful because you have dealt with it.

After doing this, or as an alternative to the above you can move onto focus about something else. It might be another issue, but I find it helpful to focus on something that you can be thankful for. For instance, you could concentrate on one or more of these things: - your health, your job, your family, your partner, Nature, food, music and so on. The list is endless. The important thing here is to focus on something that is positive and not negative as positivity lifts the spirits.

Alternatively, your meditation could be the second type where you completely clear your mind of all thoughts and distractions, sitting still, just listening to your breathing. This is so hard to do at first and will take time for you to master it, but those who regularly practise this form of meditation swear by it, saying it gives them a great sense of peace and calm.

How long should I meditate for?

"How long should I be meditating for?" is a common question many people ask. If you are a beginner, I would say five to ten minutes is sufficient. As you become more experienced and confident you could move up to around twenty minutes or more. Of course, you can't really time this as you will be meditating, but you know what I mean. With anything new it takes lots of practice and will power, but in the end it is worth it.

Closing down

Once you have decided that you have come to the end of your meditation session it is important that you bring the session to a close gradually, in an ordered way. It is best not to suddenly stop and then get up and get on with the rest of your day. Once you have decided to call it a day, keep your eyes closed (if they have been closed for your meditation session) and keep your breathing steady. Imagine shutting your Third Eye down such as shutting a door or bringing a drawbridge up. Consciously think that you have finished your session and perhaps do as I do and say a quick "Thank you" before opening your eyes. You could alternatively try counting down from 10 to 1 in your mind before you open your eyes.

After you have opened your eyes it is best to sit there for a few more minutes whilst you gather your thoughts and your eyes become accustomed to the light once more. If you have a glass of water handy you could have a quick drink. Maybe go over in your mind what that particular meditation session has taught you? What is the "Something" that you have learnt or sorted out or gained in knowledge? As you sit still think of yourself waking up after a sleep. Then once you feel that you're back in the land of the living, get up and go back to you whatever you need to do next, secure in the knowledge that you feel much more positive and equipped for whatever happens to you during the rest of the day.

5 USING COLOURS IN MEDITATION

This chapter looks at how using colours can help you in meditation. This can be one of two things. The first is a way of helping you to move your thoughts away from the everyday world and into your meditative state. The second is where you can use your whole meditation session focussing on just one colour and some of the things associated with that colour. Sometimes you might get a strong impression of a colour coming into your vision as you meditate, and the list of colours below may be useful in seeing what the significance of that colour could mean to you.

Why use colours in your meditations?

I find using colours in my meditations helpful in helping me to "get in the zone" of meditation and I always start my meditations by focussing on a colour. I find that it helps me to focus on the task in hand. It helps me to shut off all my thoughts of what is going on in my life and to focus on my meditation instead.

How exactly does this process work? When you focus your mind on a particular subject or thing, you are hopefully focussing your mind 100% on that thing. For instance, when you are taking a photograph you focus completely on that task. Or when you drive a car, you focus on driving your car, otherwise you may well crash the car. So, when you use a certain colour as a focus in your meditations, you are teaching your mind to stop thinking about the other things going on in your life and to focus on just the one thing. In this case - a certain colour.

This is why some religions when then they teach meditation, they get the person to say a certain word or a mantra, over and over again. The purpose of this is to make the mind not think of anything else but focus on that particular thing.

Once you have started to focus on your colour, you can choose to stick with that colour and see where it takes you. Or on the other hand you can let go of that colour and move onto another subject. Perhaps you want to clear your mind altogether and just have an empty mind instead. Having a colour in your mind as you start your meditation is almost like going through a door. It is best thought of as a gateway into meditation, which bridges the gap between the busy world you come from into the calm, clear world of your meditation.

Just how do I choose a colour? Well usually as I am about to begin my meditation a colour comes into my head without me thinking as I am so used to doing this, and so I concentrate on that colour to begin with. However, if this does not work for you, you could decide to choose a different colour for each day of the week. For example, blue could be the colour you use for Monday, whilst red could be for Tuesday, and so on. Below are some pointers to help you get started on this particular aspect of meditation.

Using the colours of objects in meditation

Over the years I have found that thinking of an object around the house or something in my life that I am familiar with, helps my mind to focus more easily on a particular colour. Here are some pointers. It could be a piece of furniture in your house or a wall painted in that particular colour. It could be the colour of your car or bike, or a handbag or a coat, or an umbrella perhaps. It could be the colour of a sports team such as Liverpool playing in red shirts and shorts, or Chelsea playing in blue shirts and shorts. Or it could be the colour that a house is painted in or maybe a favourite flower or food. Finally, there are many gemstones of varying colours that people find helpful in their meditations. The important thing is to get your mind to focus on that colour as you start your meditation session.

There are lots of different colours that you can use in your meditations, so here is a list of the principal colours for you to use and the thinking behind each one. Once I have decided on an actual colour, to help me focus on that colour, I begin by thinking of something associated with that colour. For example, for green I might think of a lawn all freshly cut, or perhaps some trees in the height of summer, all coloured green in a wood or forest. Or for yellow, I might think of the sun, or a lemon for example. The important thing is to get your mind to focus on that colour and not the object itself, as it is the colour which will then be used as a gateway into your meditation. Remember these are merely gateways to help you focus on a particular colour to help you gain a stronger focus in your meditation.

Caution is needed here

A word of warning though. Whilst I have used lots of colours in my meditations over the years, there is one "colour" that I never use and that is black. Some people might say that it is not really a colour per se. Black is the colour that "covers" or gets rid of any other colour. Black is the colour of the night-time and going to sleep and so if you did use it you might end up nodding off!

Certainly, black has connotations with darkness and dark powers and death for instance. The idea of using colours in your meditations is to let light into your meditation experience. Sure, you might have some colours which are darker than others, but none of these are completely dark in the way that black is. So, it is best avoided.

The colours that you can use

Now let's look at the main colours in more detail, starting with the three primary colours (as in art). I have listed in each colour section something that you associate with that colour such as a flower, or a type of fruit or vegetable for example. Remember that in many traditions each colour has a particular function or energy, which is worth remembering, especially if you practise the second type that I mentioned earlier. I have included that aspect below.

Here are the three primary colours followed by many other colours that are formed by a mixture of these basic three colours. There are also many other colours not mentioned here that you could use if you wish. The choice is up to you.

Red
Red is the colour of blood and as such is associated with the life force flowing through the body. It is also the colour of passion and commitment. There are plenty of flowers which are red including poppies, roses, and carnation. Then there are also lots of fruits that are red including strawberries, raspberries, and tomatoes. Plenty of football teams play in red including Liverpool, Arsenal and Manchester United for example. So, there are lots of different things associated with the colour red which can be helpful in your meditations.

Blue

Blue is the colour of the sea and the sky and as such represents security, honesty, and loyalty. It can also be associated with peace and tranquillity. Unfortunately, there are very few foods that are blue. You can have blueberries, but some people argue that these are more purple than blue. With flowers you can have blue pansies, hydrangea, and dahlias. There are also several football teams whose dominant colour is blue including Chelsea, Everton, and Leicester City.

The problem with blue is that is has been split up into three different dominant shades of blue – royal blue, navy blue and sky blue, so you will have to focus on just one particular shade of blue if you choose to use blue in your meditations. The term "Royal Blue" and its derivative "blue blood" is perhaps the shade of blue that we most associate with the colour blue. (Your veins actually do look blue as your blood flows through them, though this is due to the fact that our veins are reflecting more blue light back to the outside world). There is one thing in our bodies that is coloured blue that some people have and that is the blue in your eyes!

Yellow

The third primary colour yellow is the colour which most people associate with the sun. The sun gives us light and is permanently there in space shining on Earth, although we may not see it shining every day. So yellow is associated with warmth, clarity, and optimism. There are whole hosts of flowers and foods that are yellow including daffodils, tulips, sunflowers, melons, sweet corn, bananas, and lemons. In the animal kingdom you get yellow birds such as canaries, yellowhammer, and yellow wagtail. Finally, the football team Norwich City has yellow as the main colour in its shirts.

Green

Green is formed when blue and yellow are mixed together, but it is a strong colour, nevertheless. It is primarily associated with growth hence the green stems of most flowers as well as leaves and the grass. It is also associated with renewal, good health, fertility, and prosperity. Although you do not think of green flowers as such, there are some such as carnation, chrysanthemum and gladioli. Fruits and vegetables include limes, avocados, asparagus, sprouts and cucumbers.

Orange

Orange could also be the colour of the sun at sunset or sunrise and is a mixture of the colours red and yellow. As such it represents the qualities of enthusiasm, spontaneity, optimism, and creativity. Flowers that are orange include marigolds and dahlias. Fruits include oranges (of course!), peaches and tangerines. Again, there are plenty of orange coloured vegetables including carrots, sweet potatoes, and pumpkins. Orang-utans are perhaps the best-known orange coloured animal, but there are also tigers, squirrels, foxes, and iguana. Finally, there are some football teams that play in orange including Blackpool and the Dutch national team.

Pink

Pink is formed by combining the colours of red and white. It has long been associated with the feminine side but has many other qualities. These include love, romance, nurturing, compassion and understanding. There are some flowers that are pink including carnations, hyacinths, roses, dahlias, tulips and of course the flower known as a pink. Apart from rhubarb, there are hardly any fruit and vegetables that are noticeably pink. There are some animals and birds that are pink, notably flamingos, pigs and cockatoos.

Sky Blue

Sky blue is a mixture of blue and white and as its name suggests is the colour of the sky that we see from Earth, as well as the sea in some parts of the world. It is quite a calming colour and its qualities include stability, loyalty, wisdom, intelligence, and truth. Flowers that are sky blue include hydrangeas, the iris, delphinium, and orchids. Sports teams that play in sky blue shirts include Manchester City and Coventry City.

Purple

This is formed from mixing red and blue and again has various shades. Its qualities include power, luxury, wealth, imagination, ambition, and extravagance. Flowers include dahlias, pansies, lavender, and the iris. Fruits include blackberries and blueberries. Vegetables include beetroot, eggplant and cabbage.

Brown

Brown is associated most strongly with the earth from which all things grow and to which human and animal waste matter is returned. It is a mixture of black and red and has the qualities of strength, reliability, safety, and resilience. Foods that are brown include rice, dates, various nuts, and some cooked meats. Plenty of animals are brown in colour, partly as a result of camouflage and these include bears, horses, alpacas, dogs, sheep, and monkeys.

Grey

Grey is formed by mixing black and white and as such is seen as rather a drab colour. For instance, we associate grey skies with a dull day with no sunlight coming through. Grey can be associated with the formal - as in a suit, and a conservative attitude, though it can also be associated with sophistication and timelessness. Presumably, because it has black in it some associate it with dirtiness and depression. Grey can also be thought of as intelligent due to the colour of the brain, or it can be connected with old age due to older people's hair turning to that colour.

White

Although white is considered to be a colour by some and not a colour by others, I have included it here as not only do all the other colours merge or blend to form white, but it is also seen as having a protection side to it. The qualities of white are naturally purity, but it also is seen as innocence, honesty, cleanliness, and neutrality. Flowers that are white include the lily, carnations, roses, daisies, camellia, hibiscus, and lily of the valley. Foods that are white include rice, egg white (when cooked), bread (the inside), onions and cauliflowers. Sports teams include Leeds United, Tottenham Hotspur and the England national team.

How to use colours in your meditation

Now having decided on a colour, let me explain how you can use that colour in meditation. As mentioned earlier I always start my meditation with a different colour each day. So, having decided on a colour, what is the next step?

If using a colour to help you to get into your meditation session this is what I do. I imagine the colour as a mist or a liquid that gradually comes towards me and envelops me until I am completely covered by this colour. Then I open up to this colour so that it comes inside me, and I am now one with the colour. Those of you who are spiritually minded can think of this of opening up your Third Eye so that you are united with the Universe or Spirit or God or whatever force you believe in. If this isn't for you, just think of this as where you have left the world behind and you are now starting your meditation. You can then proceed in one of two ways. You could discard the colour in your mind and think that you are now in the zone, so your meditation can get going with whatever subject you want to focus on.

Or you could stay with that colour and use it as the basis for your meditation. For example, if you chose to focus on the colour green you could start by thinking of green things such as leaves, the grass, or vegetables. Green is the colour that is most associated with growth and energy. For instance, you know that a leaf is alive and full of energy when it is green. When it turns to yellow or brown you know that it is dying or dead. So perhaps think grateful thoughts here of how the leaves help you in the process of photosynthesis, giving out oxygen to you and taking away your carbon dioxide, thus helping the world to breathe in a way. Next you could think about how the green vegetables that you eat, be they lettuce, cabbage, or beans, all give you energy and help you to be healthy.

As you think more about things that are green you can achieve a sense of thankfulness and gratitude for these things. If you think positive thoughts about these things, you in turn will become a more positive person. So, when you emerge from your meditation you will have hopefully achieved something that has helped you to be a more grateful, appreciative, and positive person.

Once you have finished your meditation, don't forget to close yourself down safely. If you opened your Third Eye at the start of your meditation session now is the time to close it. If not, you could say either out loud or in your mind, "My meditation session has finished" or simply, "Thank you" or whatever else you choose to say. Then wait a few minutes as you "wake up" or come back into everyday life. Hopefully using colours in either of these ways will have helped you.

6 USING CHAKRAS IN MEDITATION

What are the Chakras and where do they come from?

The word "Chakra" comes from the Sanskrit word meaning 'wheel' or 'disc' and so chakras can be thought of as wheels turning round within your body. Although they cannot be seen as such, most people who accept them as being part of your spiritual or etheric body say they can feel their energy and their life force. They say that they connect your spiritual body to the material body as psychic energy centres. Most people who accept the concept of the chakras agree that there are seven main or key chakras, each of which has a specific function. They are situated in the centre of the body, starting at the base of the spine and going upwards to the top of the head, along the primary "nadi" or channel of energy. There are however believed to be more chakras at different parts of the body, which I will discuss further on in this chapter.

Although the idea of the chakras came from Hindu sacred texts known as the Upanishads going back to approximately 2,500 years ago, it was only at the beginning of the twentieth century that they became popularised in the West. This was largely due to the writings of Charles W. Leadbeater and Alice Bailey, who were members of the Theosophical Society. In particular they both saw the importance of how the chakras can influence the human body and of their connection with the endocrine system.

Why are the Chakras connected with meditation?

The chakras are used in meditation (and yoga) partly because that is what many people in the East have been doing for thousands of years, and partly because it can be argued that they are in some way connected with the body's endocrine system, which I discuss below.

Those who believe in this concept, state that when you meditate, if you involve the chakras in your meditation, it will help to relieve or cure any illnesses in the human body, both physical and emotional. Using the chakras in a meditation is sometimes called "Chakra balancing" as these seven chakras can often become blocked or not balanced properly in our etheric body due to emotional or physical trauma within our physical body. By carefully re-balancing these chakras through meditation, you will ultimately be healing the emotional and physical body at the same time.

Let's now look in more detail at the chakras and what they represent.

The Chakras and what they do

According to some experts there are over a hundred different chakras found in the body, each one representing an energy centre at a particular point within your body. Apart from the chakras there are thousands of "Nadis" which are a type of "distribution network" for divine energy throughout the human body. This concept is also prevalent in Traditional Chinese medicine where the "qi" or life force flows through meridians all over the body. It aims to rebalance the yin (or passive force) with the yang (or active force) within the body. With chakra balancing or healing most spiritual teachers and religious traditions tend to focus on the seven core chakras, and these have been used in meditation for centuries.

Starting at the lowest chakra and going up through the body the seven main chakras are: -

The Base Chakra or Muladhara
This is sometimes called the Root Chakra in some traditions as it is found at the base of your spine and upholds your whole body and chakra system which should be in balance. As such it is involved with your relationship with the world around you, as well as your basic needs of food, shelter and stability. Its colour is red.

The Sacral Chakra or Svadhisthana
Sometimes known as the Navel or Sexual Chakra, this chakra is found just below your navel and is connected with your reproductive or sexual organs. It is also concerned with your imagination and your creativity. If it is not balanced, you will have difficulty in coping with new experiences that may come your way. Its colour is orange.

The Solar Plexus Chakra or Manipura
This chakra is found just above your navel in your stomach area. As such it is connected to your digestive system. If there is imbalance here, you can feel tenseness and worry. Its colour is yellow.

The Heart Chakra or Anahata
This chakra is found in your heart area, which is the centre of your body's cardiovascular system. If there is imbalance here, you could have high blood pressure or respiratory problems. It is also the chakra where love flows out of you to other people. Its colour is green.

The Throat Chakra or Vishuddha
This chakra is situated in your throat area near the thyroid glands and helps you with self-expression and communication. If this chakra is not in balance you can become lonely and susceptible to hormonal imbalance and infections. Its colour is blue.

The Third Eye Chakra or Ajna
The Third Eye chakra is situated in the middle of your forehead, just above the centre of your eyebrows. This chakra is said to be a guide to your intuition in both a spiritual and a material aspect of yourself. If you keep this third eye chakra in balance you will have the ability to see your place in the world around, you and how you fit into it. Its colour is indigo.

The Crown Chakra or Sahasrara
This final chakra is situated at the top of your head and is thought of as being the main chakra as it links you with the Universe or God. Like a crown that a king or queen wears, so the Crown Chakra is found in the same position in the region of the top of your head. It is associated with the colours white and purple.

The Endocrine System and the Chakras

Many people believe that these seven main chakras actually correspond to the main parts of the endocrine system in the human body, each of which has a certain function. The Endocrine System is a network of glands within your body that produce the hormones needed for a well-functioning body. These move into the bloodstream and help with bodily functions like growth, reproduction, and metabolism.

The main parts of the endocrine system starting in the brain and going down the body are as follows: -

The Hypothalamus
The Hypothalamus is situated inside the brain, helping to maintain the body's internal balance, known as homeostasis. It is also the body's link between the endocrine and nervous systems. It helps to maintain a balance within many of the body's main processes including blood pressure, body temperature and appetite.

The Pituitary Gland
The Pituitary Gland can be found at the base of the brain and secretes hormones which help to regulate the functions of the other endocrine glands. It is sometimes known at the "master gland" because its hormones control some of the other glands in the endocrine system, though in reality it in turn is stimulated by the hypothalamus.

The Pineal Gland
The Pineal Gland is situated in the centre of the brain and was once known as the "Third Eye". It produces melatonin which helps to maintain the circadian (or biological) rhythm of your body and to regulate the reproductive hormones.

The Thyroid Gland
The Thyroid Gland has the function of regulating your metabolism which is about breaking down the food that you eat and converting it into energy. It is situated just in front of the windpipe and just below the Adam's Apple in the neck.

The Thymus
The Thymus is responsible for the production of T-cells, a type of white blood cell which protects the growing body from infections and viruses. Once you reach puberty it starts to shrink and is gradually replaced by fat. It is situated in the front part of your chest behind your sternum and between your lungs.

The Adrenal Glands

The Adrenal Glands are two glands that are found on top of your kidneys inside your body. The first, the adrenal cortex produces glands including cortisol which helps your body to respond to stress and aldosterone which helps to control blood pressure. The second, the adrenal medulla produces non-essential hormones like adrenaline which helps your body to combat stress.

The Pancreas

The Pancreas is situated deep inside the body between the stomach and the spine. It has the function of maintaining the body's blood glucose or sugar levels. The main hormone it produces is insulin which helps to maintain the balance of blood sugar (glucose) and salt inside your body.

The Ovaries and Testes

The Ovaries and Testes are part of the female and male reproductive system respectively. The ovaries have the function of producing estrogen and progesterone which help to maintain the health of the female reproductive system. They are found on either side of the uterus on the pelvic wall. The testes on the other hand produce the hormone testosterone which is important for the proper development of male physical characteristics. They are found inside a sac called the scrotum which hangs outside of the body behind the penis.

Having looked at the function of each of these parts of the endocrine system, this is how they are connected with the chakras.

The adrenal gland is associated with the base/root chakra
The ovaries and testes are related to the sacral/navel chakra
The pancreas is associated with the solar plexus
The thymus is related to the heart chakra
The thyroid gland relates to the throat chakra
The pituitary gland is connected with the third eye chakra
The pineal gland is associated with the crown chakra

Please note that some traditions have the pineal gland connected to the third eye chakra, and the pituitary gland connected to the crown chakra. Some traditions see the Hypothalamus as connected to the third eye chakra, whilst others see it as being an overall part of the chakra system. They still use it in their chakra meditations either at the beginning or the end of their meditation session as a kind of guiding chakra for the others.

How to use the chakras/endocrine system in your meditation

Whether you accept the chakras as being real or not, it is always useful in your meditations to spend time thinking about the endocrine system and how each part has a function which affects your body and helps to keep it healthy and energised. So, I have devised a meditation where both the chakras and the endocrine system can be used. If you want to leave out the chakra part of the meditation, that is up to you.

This is how I use the chakras when I practise meditation. After entering into a state of relaxation, I start with the crown chakra/pineal gland and then make my way down through the other chakras/glands one by one through to the base chakra. At each chakra I stop and pause for a few minutes imagining that particular chakra glowing with life, turning steadily, and emitting a strong energy. You can of course begin at the other end with the base chakra/adrenal gland and move upwards chakra by chakra (or gland by gland) if you want. If you don't want to use the chakras you can do this meditation by just using the glands of the endocrine system instead.

So, in more detail these are some of the things I think about at each stage: -

Crown chakra/pineal gland
This is involved with integrating all the other endocrine glands and helps run the whole show if you like. It is also about our understanding of everything around us, so think about your brain and intelligence and how you process information. What is it that you are allowing into your mind and your body? Is it positive and good for you? Or is it negative and not good for you?

Third eye chakra/pituitary gland
This gland is often associated with our psychic side or our intuition and as such many see it as important in helping us to react to certain outside influences. The pituitary gland helps to synchronise our internal rhythms and maintain our hormone levels. So, think about being balanced and all things working correctly within your body. Also think about how you react to certain situations. Is there something you can do to overcome any fears that you may have?

Throat chakra/thyroid gland
This gland is important in maintaining our metabolism and helping us to recover properly after physical activity. Think about feeling balanced and harmonious as well as how the throat is where sound comes from. So perhaps think about how you communicate with others and what you say. Is it positive or negative? Does it help someone or hinder them?

Heart chakra/thymus
This is concerned with our ability to give out love and to overcome any fear in our life. The heart in many ways is the life force which keeps the body alive, so give thanks for all it does, especially in pumping blood around the body. Think of it as protecting you from the outside world.

Solar plexus chakra/pancreas
This is concerned with our own power and how we fit into the world. Imagine that you are strong and cannot be bullied or coerced into doing something you do not want to do. Body wise

the pancreas governs our use of energy within the body so imagine your food giving you the correct amount of energy for your needs. Imagine that you are balanced and not tired or irritable.

Sacral chakra/ovaries and testes
These two glands are about our sexuality and our ability to reproduce as well as to feel sexual pleasure. Think about being balanced sexually. You are neither addicted to sex, nor afraid of it or see it as sinful. Also think about how you could use your body to create another human being and the responsibility that it brings.

Base chakra/adrenal gland
This gland is connected with our understanding of the physical world and our safety and security within it. So, think about how secure and grounded you feel. Perhaps think about where you live and the safety that living in a house provides you. Body wise think about how well your body is functioning and feeling fine, with all parts of the body working as they should be.

Please note that in some traditions the sacral chakra is associated with the adrenal gland, whilst the base chakra is associated with the ovaries and the testes.

As I concentrate on each chakra/gland in my body, I am thinking about healing going on in both in my mind and in my body, as well as energising energy making me strong and fit and well. Once I have finished, I might continue my meditation in a heightened state, going onto another subject or object to focus on. Or I might close down the meditation altogether. You could choose to focus on one different chakra/gland on each day of the week as there are seven. Or you could quickly go through each chakra one by one, either from the bottom or the top and visualise each one turning perfectly and functioning correctly as a precursor before you start your meditation proper. Again, the choice is yours.

Other chakras

Some teachers and traditions say that there are other chakras in and around the body apart from the seven most important ones. You could incorporate these into your meditations either as an alternative chakra meditation or as an addition to the main chakra meditation above. Here is some information about these.

The Earth Star Chakra is said to be situated eleven inches below your feet and is the chakra which connects you to Mother Earth. It helps you to feel connected to Planet Earth.

The Core Star Chakra is located near the diaphragm just above the sacral chakra. It represents our interest in esoteric knowledge and helps us to understand our position in the world.

The Sacred Heart Chakra is situated below and just to the left of the heart chakra. It helps us to give out unconditional love and to expand our consciousness.

The Thymus Chakra is found in the area between the heart and the throat and is sometimes known as the higher heart chakra. It helps you to see beauty in all things and to access Divine Love.

The Cerebellum Chakra is found at the back of the neck at the point where head and neck meet. It helps you to access your creative ideas and your soul contract.

The Pineal Chakra is said to be situated behind the eyes in the centre of the brain and helps you to become more spiritually aware.

The Soul Star Chakra can be found just above the crown chakra and is connected with your past lives and karma.

The God's Head Chakra is found about twelve inches above the crown chakra. It helps to bring in God energy and show you a higher consciousness.

The above is just one alternative to the traditional chakra system. Another one has twelve chakras with the traditional seven chakras plus these five others: - the Earth Chakra, the Lunar Chakra, the Solar Chakra, the Galactic Chakra and the Universal Chakra. So you can see that there are several other chakras according to which belief system you belong to.

In the next chapter I talk about guided meditation and how it can help you. I also show you several guided meditations that you can practise at home or outside if you wish.

7 GUIDED MEDITATIONS

How to start with a guided meditation

When you do a guided meditation, you are being led or guided by someone else, perhaps in person, or via a recording, or just by reading some guidance notes, as in this book. There are literally thousands of subjects that you can base your meditations on. Choosing one is really just a question of what is on your mind, or what weighs heavy on your heart. There are thousands to be found on the internet; some are free and some you have to pay for. Beware of websites or articles that begin with, "This is a great meditation for….." though. They may well be a great meditation for the person who created them, but are they great for you? Are they really trying to sell you a meditation that you don't really need? So, use your intuition whenever you are looking at websites that advertise meditations.

Sometimes in my meditations I tend to concentrate on one particular subject or theme that is on my mind, such as a problem I have that I need a solution to. I find that by doing this it helps me to overcome a problem or a struggle that I might be facing in my life at that time. At other times I may just focus on an abstract theme or word, like "Love", or "Peace" and see where I go with that.

The thing with guided meditations is learning to be flexible. You can just "go with the flow" as they say and go where your heart leads you. You don't have to stick to the script if you don't want to. All the guided meditations below contain pointers and suggestions of what you can use in your meditations. You may choose to follow them to the letter, or you may just pick one or two ideas from them and go from there. The choice is yours.

Examples of guided meditations

Here are two examples of guided meditations which hopefully will show you the way forward. For example, I might choose to concentrate on the theme of Forgiveness. So, as you move into your guided meditation begin to think about the people who you may have upset or hurt, either by what you might have said, or by an action that you did that you later regretted. Or on the other hand you could be thinking about someone who has hurt or upset you. Can you forgive them? Or are you not able to do so yet because you are hanging onto the hurt from them? Finally, think about the effect that forgiveness has on you, hopefully releasing you from anger and hurt, and giving you the power to move on with your life.

It is through doing this guided meditation that you might gain the insight you are looking for to move on. Perhaps it might help you to make your peace with someone or learn to forgive and forget something that has caused you hurt in the past. The important thing is that something positive will hopefully come out of this meditation.

On the other hand, you could choose the guided meditation on the theme of Love. You might start with looking at who has loved you in your life? You could go through each family member one by one, recognising where they have shown love to you and asking yourself why you have loved them. You might start with your mother and father, then maybe your grandparents, or a brother or a sister if you had them in your family. Moving on, maybe you could look at a boyfriend or girlfriend that loved you. Did you love them or were you taking them for a ride? Then if you fell in love, was it mutual and did you live happily ever after? Or did something go wrong? Have you overcome the hurt that you might have felt? Next you might consider the best friends that you have had in your life. What was it about them that you liked, admired, and ultimately loved them for?

That is one way to go with love, but there are plenty of other ways, such as love for this planet, love for your enemies, and love for people who have a specific role to play in life like politicians, councillors, teachers, doctors, nurses and so on. Or you could think about what love actually means. Is it an abstract thing? Or is it something more specific? Think about the different types of love that you could meditate on. Finally, you could think about how love changes people and ultimately the world.

From these two examples, you should be able to see that from just one word or concept or idea you can go in several different directions. You can choose to be rigid and stick with just the one aspect of something, or you can be more flexible and branch out in more than one direction.

Below are some different guided meditations which you might like to try. Obviously, some of them might not be to your taste, so if you want to give them a miss that is ok. Perhaps by trying some of them you will be inspired to try some other subject that you can think of.

Some guided meditations

Here are some guided meditations that you can try if you so wish. Please don't forget to get into the meditative state first, and afterwards close yourself down. You could read through the suggestions first before you start, or you could take this book with you and when you are ready, refer to it to help you in your meditation. Some may be relevant to you and what interests you, whilst others may not. Just leave those ones out and concentrate on those you empathise with.

The Natural World

This is one meditation that is ideal for you to do when you are sitting outside or having a walk, although it could be part of your regular meditation sessions indoors. Nature is something that we very often take for granted, yet it is all around us, such as birds flying past our house or a tree growing and changing with the seasons. Maybe ask yourself, "How often do I notice the natural world all around me?" or "Do I really appreciate Nature and all the good things that it provides for me?" Sometimes when I am on a train or a bus journey that takes me through the countryside, I meditate on all that I can see out of the window and it helps me to be more appreciative of the natural world.

You can start by looking at and thinking about the scenery around you, whether you are at home or on a journey. If you are at home, think about your garden or street or local park and what natural things you can see. It could be the birds, as they seem to be everywhere! It could be trees and flowers or bushes. It could be a stream or a river that flows near to your home. Or it could be the animal world, be it wildlife like a squirrel or a fox, or domestic animals like dogs and cats. You could focus on one or more of these things and think about what they give out to you, whether it be beauty, comfort, companionship or just entertainment!

If you are living out in the countryside or are on a journey, there will most likely be plenty of fields and trees to see, perhaps a river or a pond. If you are going through a really wild place there might well be hills and mountains, or lakes and forests. Be thankful for all that you see and how nice it is to be in the countryside. You could then move onto all the different animal life that is out there. If you start with birds you could think of their beauty, such as their colour as seen on their feathers or their wings. As you watch the birds in flight you might think how fantastic it is how they fly. You could then move onto their nests in the trees and their ingenuity in building them out of all the various materials found in the countryside.

In many parts of the world, you are quite likely to see sheep and cows grazing in the fields, ultimately providing the meat eaters among us with food. There might also be horses, or dogs out walking, or wild animals such as foxes or rabbits, or other animals depending on where you are in the world. Try and be thankful for all these things and feel appreciation for them, for they all have a place and a purpose in our world.

Next, look at all the different things that grow from the ground. Trees are probably the most common thing you will see. Think of all that oxygen that they give out and the carbon dioxide that they take in so that we can all breathe. That's a very big thing to think about, as without the trees we would find it hard to survive. Then there are plenty of other things that grow such as grass, bushes, and flowers. With the latter you might try and think about all the bees that are busy in the summer helping to pollinate most of our fruit and vegetables. Again, without them we would find it hard to survive.

Finally, observe the landscape. Perhaps you are in awe of the sight of a mountain or a lake as you travel on your journey? Or you might notice lots of green fields or golden cornfields, or some colourful bushes or clumps of flowers. Ask yourself what emotion does it stir up in you? Beauty? Peace? Tranquillity perhaps? Depending on what time of the year you are in, you might be aware of a particular season, such as snow covering the ground in winter, or all the leaves falling from the trees in autumn/fall. It is worth remembering that the seasons are always happening around us, maybe not as clearly as they used to be, due to climate change, but whatever time of the year it is there are always plenty of things out there that you can be thankful for.

This is only a fraction of the natural world that I have covered here. Again, you might like to focus on just a few of these things. What is important to remember is that we are all part of a web that connects us all in some way and if we destroy one part of that web then we all ultimately pay the price for this.

Learning to love yourself

In this meditation you will explore your own inner self, your body, and your whole attitude to yourself. Ask yourself, "How do I feel about my body? Is there something that I don't like? Is there a part of my body that I would like to change? If you answer "Yes" to these last two questions, perhaps you might like to think about how useful your body is to you and how it helps you in so many ways.

First of all, try and be thankful for your body. Think about all the different parts and their functions – your arms and legs and feet, your heart, lungs, and brain for a start. Then there are your fingers and toes, your hair and your teeth; your eyes and ears and all the senses connected with these parts. Next think about how interconnected they all are – how when you use one part, the other parts are affected in some way. Then you could think about how your body grows in size from a tiny baby, through to being a child, then a teenager and finally into an adult. As you start to be appreciative of your body, you might start to change the way you think about it.

If you start to look in more detail at some of your body parts, at what job they do, or at all the various cells and veins and nodes that make up a particular body part, then perhaps you might start to love your body in a way that you never thought of before. Maybe you can start to be more appreciative of your body and how it works and so love yourself.

Vision for a better world

This is quite a large and wide-ranging subject, but not one that many of us actually think about. Ask yourself, "Am I so entrenched in my life, my work, my relationships and so on, that I don't think about the type of world that I would like to be living in?" Many of us tend to think that the world revolves around us and that what we see and experience is the extent of what is going on in the world. Ask yourself if you ever watch the news from beginning to end? Or do you read about the situation in a particular country? Maybe you think that the whole situation is hopeless and there is nothing that you can do to make a difference.

Hopefully, if you are meditating on a regular basis, you will have learnt that there is more to you than you ever realised before you started meditating. You may also have started to notice the state of the world as well. Millions of humans think this thought every day, so you are not alone here.

This meditation is designed to help you think more deeply about this and how you yourself might be part of this change. Where do you start though? Do you want peace everywhere? Or would you like to see an end to poverty or starvation? Or is the state of the environment something which concerns you? Whatever you choose from these or any other issue that is going on in the world, then that can be your starting point.

If it is peace that you want above everything else, start by visualising all people living in peace and loving each other, free from war and conflict. Perhaps you can visualise people from different races or religions shaking hands, hugging each other, or sitting down and having a meal together. Or it could be certain world leaders or politicians doing the same thing. What about all the weapons that are being made? Perhaps you could visualise all the weapons melting, or the nuclear bombs being made harmless, or all the arms factories being shut down? These are just some things that could happen if peace is to be achieved. There are doubtless other things that you could visualise to do with peace, so see where your meditation takes you.

You could then move on from here to seeing a world where there is enough food to go round for everybody. Ask yourself how could this be achieved? Visualise the leaders of the rich countries deciding to do something about this and planes taking off with food to go to those countries where there isn't enough food. Or visualise food experts teaching local people how to get the best out of their land. Or see irrigation schemes being implemented in countries where there isn't enough rainfall to irrigate the land.

Finally, what about the environment? What about all those forests being cut down so cattle can graze, or other crops can be grown on the cleared land? Or what about all the wildlife that is finding nowhere to live as their natural habitat has been destroyed? Instead, visualise all these things being reversed with trees being planted, people choosing not to eat meat, and wild animals having plenty of natural areas to live in, free from danger. You could also visualise the leaders of countries saying "No" to industries and practises that destroy the environment.

With all of these issues, as well as others that I haven't mentioned here there are already many people doing something about this in joining campaign groups, signing petitions or getting involved in local and national politics. Perhaps through meditating on these issues you might be led into doing something yourself and thus make a difference in your own small way?

The Stars and Space

This meditation is best done outside at night, preferably in the summer when it is warm enough to sit outside; though it can be done at other times of the year if you wrap up warm. You might like to do it in your garden if you have one, but only do it if you are in a safe place. If not, you could do it looking out of your window instead. The main thing is that it must be a clear night with no clouds, so that you can see the stars. If it is a full moon the night sky will be bright, but it would be better when the moon is not full, as you can see more detail then.

Start by getting your mind focussed. You could close your eyes at first whilst you clear your mind. Then when you are ready, open them and look upwards. Ask yourself what do you see? Don't just think, "Stars!", but allow yourself to take in the vision in front of you. Think to yourself, "What an amazing sight!" Just think about the fact that the Universe that you are looking at goes on and on for ever? It may well be mind-blowing to you but recognise the fact that you are still special. You, a human being living on this tiny speck of a planet in this vast, fathomless universe are still important and you have a role to play in the world.

Now if you start to think about some of the problems in your life, you begin to realize that they are so insignificant compared to the vastness up there. Think about how the stars are just like our sun, all alive in their own unique way, giving light and power to the planets and the darkness that surrounds them.

You could think about the power of the Universe as you look up. It may cause you to think about where you come from and how everything began. It might even cause you to think of the question, "Who made it all? Or did it just evolve gradually out of nothing? If you are religious, you might find yourself saying a prayer of thanks to the god that you believe in. Or if not, just think of how you fit into all of this.

How much time you spend outside or just observing the night sky is up to you, but as with all meditations bring it to a close in your mind in whatever way you choose before you come in. Afterwards, you might like to try and find out more about space and the planets, perhaps through astronomy or even astrology. The important thing is that you realise that you are a part of this vast place we call the universe.

These then are just a few of the thousands of guided meditations that you can use in your meditations. Others might involve the subjects of your job, your career, prosperity, relationships, romance, money, moving to a new house, children, parents and so on. Or you could choose to meditate on a more abstract subject like love, peace, kindness, gratitude, generosity, or healing. I would avoid a negative subject though, as this does not serve you or anyone. If you are in conflict with someone for instance, you could use your meditation to find release or closure from this situation. Or if you have been hurt deeply by someone, rather than focussing on the hurt, concentrate on a positive outcome such as forgiveness, justice or letting go of it. If there is something that is not mentioned here you could try looking it up on the internet under "guided meditation on....." and I am sure that you will more often than not find it.

8 FINAL THOUGHTS

What have I learnt?

As you come to the end of this book and have hopefully started to meditate yourself, you could now ask the question, "What have I learnt?" "Have I understood all that I have read?" If not, is there somewhere else that you could turn to, to find the answer? This chapter will hopefully give you some pointers of where you can go to next.

By taking this first step into meditation, you should have started to grow in confidence and are meditating every day or at least meditating on most days. Perhaps you have started to meditate for longer periods? Ask yourself, "Do I feel more confident in myself? Do I feel calmer? Has practising meditation helped me to solve some of the problems in my life?" There are perhaps other questions that you might well be asking at this stage, which you haven't yet answered. Learning to meditate is not something that you will master overnight or even in a few weeks, so apart from persevering with you meditation, what else can you do? What is the next step? Here are some pointers.

Taking things a step further

As mentioned earlier in the book there are plenty of online resources about meditation. You might like to look at some of these if you are thinking of widening your horizons and trying out new meditations or just learning about different ways of meditating. There are also many apps that have plenty of guided meditations which you can get for your smart phone or tablet. I have included some of these in the Resources section at the end of this book.

After this, the next step maybe to try meditating with a friend or your partner - if they are agreeable. When you do try this, it can be done in the same way as you meditate when you are by yourself, though you should resist the temptation to talk to each other during the meditation, unless one of you is guiding the other in the meditation. Perhaps agree on a subject or theme that you are going to meditate on and agree who will draw the session to the end. Then once you have finished, you could discuss what you have experienced and learnt.

Apart from this, you might like to try joining a meditation group in your locality. These groups tend to meet once a week or a fortnight in a hall somewhere or at someone's house and are usually quite informal. They have guided meditations led by a meditation leader who will choose a subject for you to explore in your meditation. You might discuss with others what you experienced or what you learnt. Attending one of these sessions may well help you to go to a higher level with your meditations, but also they are a good way of getting to know like-minded people and make new friends. These sorts of groups often advertise in the windows of specialist shops or cafes, or perhaps try looking on the internet under "meditation groups in....." and see what comes up.

Some people who start doing meditation find that it leads them becoming a more spiritual person. They start to feel a connection with the world and the universe that they have never felt before. Some say that that it leads to a spiritual awakening or an interest in religion which they never had before. Some go on to practise their meditation away from their home and into a building of a particular religion, such as a Buddhist Centre or a Hindu Temple. Whilst this is not everyone's cup of tea, it is one possible way to go if you choose.

Meditation courses and retreats

Going one step further, you might like to consider going away for a few days on a meditation course or retreat. These can sometimes be just for a day in your own country or for several days abroad. Again, you will be with like-minded people who are trying to learn more about meditation, as well as having a nice little break away from it all. Some tend to concentrate solely on meditation, which can be a little intense if you are new to this. Whilst other retreats provide a mixture of activities, apart from meditation including yoga, massage, walking, cooking, etc. They are not for everyone of course, but if you are adventurous, or just want to try something different maybe one of these courses might be for you.

Many of these courses can be found by doing a quick search on the internet or are advertised in health or spirituality-based magazines. Some take place at regular intervals throughout the year, so if you are not sure about going you could see if any of them have reviews on the internet. Maybe you could go with a friend if you are wary of going by yourself? Since the Pandemic came in many of these retreat or wellness centres have started to do on-line retreats which you can join in from the comfort of your own home. This could be a way of testing the water so to speak, to see if this is for you or not. Again, I have included some links to several of these in the Resources section.

Final thoughts

So finally, we are now at the end of this book on meditation. I hope that it has been helpful to you and that you are able to take something from it. Please remember that meditation takes time to learn and cultivate, so be patient. Maybe keep a diary of your meditation experiences and then look back in a few weeks, months, or years down the line? Who knows, maybe one day you will be teaching meditation to others as a meditation teacher? You never know!

RESOURCES

Below you will find a list of various resources and contacts to do with meditation, which may be of interest to you. Always check them out thoroughly before committing or parting with your money.

Disclaimer. Please note that the links to the following apps, organisations, retreats and websites have been included in good faith. Neither the author, nor Hadleigh Books can be held responsible for the validity of these courses or retreats and what they offer; nor can they be held responsible for the content and functionality of these apps and websites, or the services that they offer.

Meditation apps
These are a few apps on the internet that may be helpful to you.
buddhify.com
calm.com
insighttimer.com
simplehabit.com
tenpercent.com
unplug.com

Meditation websites

Here are some meditation websites and pages from various organisations which promote meditation, which may be of use if you want to find out more about meditation and expand your meditation experience.

about meditation.com
headspace.com
meditatinginsafety.org.uk
meditationinitiative.org*
meditationoasis.com
meditationsociety.com
meditationtrust.com
mindful.org
spiritualengland.org.uk
studysociety.org
tm.org
wccm.org

Meditation courses and retreats

Here is a list of websites from around the world that offer courses and retreats that include meditation in their programmes. Please be aware that some of them are at religious places, though they are open to anyone of other faiths or none.

UK: -
bookmeditationretreats.com
dhanakosa.com
gaiahopuse.co.uk
holyisle.org
lbc.org.uk
rawhorizons.co.uk
sharphamtrust.org

Europe: -
assisiretreats.org
moulindechaves.org
passaddhi.com
queenofretreats.com
serenityretreat.co.uk
shambalagatherings.com
walkinginspirit.co.uk

USA/Canada: -
artoflivingretreatcenter.org
dharma.org
esalen.org
ojosantafe.ojospa.com
monastere.ca
rollingmeadowsretreat.com
shambhalamountain.org
spiritrock.org
zmm.org

Rest of the World: -
kopanmonastery.com
shaktihimalaya.com
temenos.org.za
vana.co.in
wonderlandhc.com

© Mark Chatterton/Hadleigh Books 2020

ABOUT THE AUTHOR

Mark Chatterton is an author, broadcaster, self-help teacher and workshop leader who has helped many people learn to meditate in order to live calmer, happier and more healthy lives, free from stress, anger and fear.

markchatterton.com